Professor Nutter and
THE CURSE OF THE
PHARAOH'S TOMB

by

David Webb

© David Webb 2008

The moral right of the author has been asserted in accordance with the
Copyright, Designs and Patents Act 1988

ISBN-10 1-905637-42-X
ISBN-13 978-1-905637-42-3

Educational Printing Services Limited
Albion Mill, Water Street, Great Harwood, Blackburn BB6 7QR
Telephone: (01254) 882080   Fax: (01254) 882010
E-mail: enquiries@eprint.co.uk   Website: www.eprint.co.uk

Contents

Chapter 1
The Secret Room

Professor Nutter stared with wonder and excitement into the large hole that the builder had just knocked through his bedroom wall.

'What a discovery!' he gushed, turning towards his nephew. 'It's fantastic! Do you realise how important this could be, Nigel?'

'It's a hole in the wall,' muttered Nigel,

scratching one of his spots. 'What's so exciting about a hole in the wall?'

'Yes, but it's not just *any* hole and it's not just *any* wall,' explained the Professor, peering into the darkness. 'I told you, Nigel – this house once belonged to Howard Carter.'

Nigel looked blank. He turned towards Blister the builder and his son Alfie, who was munching from a packet of salt 'n vinegar flavour crisps. They both shook their heads in ignorance.

'Howard Carter!' repeated the Professor, removing his round rimmed glasses. 'Surely you've heard of Howard Carter?'

'Was he a pop star?' asked Nigel. 'I think my mum might have some of his songs.'

'Of course he wasn't a pop star!' snapped Professor Nutter. 'What on earth do they teach you at school these days? Howard Carter was probably the most famous archaeologist who ever lived! Back in 1922, he discovered the tomb of Tutankhamun, the Boy King of Egypt.'

'And this was his house,' said Blister the builder, looking impressed. 'What do you think of that, Alfie?'

'Cool,' said Alfie, pulling another crisp from his bag. In truth, he was completely bored. 'Shall we finish bashing the wall down?'

'Take great care,' warned the Professor, replacing his glasses. 'We're breaking through into a secret room, just like Howard Carter broke through into Tutankhamun's tomb! Who knows what might be on the other side!'

'Stand back!' warned Blister, and he raised his hammer and brought it crashing down on the dry plaster wall. There was a cloud of choking dust as the builder struck again and again. Nigel covered his eyes with

his hand and Alfie covered his bag of crisps. When the dust settled there was a gap in the wall big enough to crawl through. Sure enough, beyond the gap was a small dark room, completely empty except for a heavy wooden bookcase that stood against the opposite wall.

'It's completely empty,' said Nigel, stating the obvious. 'That's not very exciting, is it?'

'I'll squeeze through and take a look,' said the Professor, sounding a little disappointed. 'Why would Howard Carter seal up an empty bookcase in a secret room?'

'Let me go first,' offered Blister the builder. 'I'll clear away the rubble for you.'

Before the Professor had a chance to reply, Blister had moved forward and was squeezing through the gap. He was a large man and it was a tight fit but, with a final grunt and groan, he pushed his way into the secret room. The Professor, Nigel and Blister's son Alfie stared after him but all they could see was the builder's dusty bottom.

'Is everything all right?' shouted Alfie. 'What's it like in there?'

'It feels strangely cold,' replied the builder, 'and the floorboards seem a bit rotten but they shouldn't be a problem.'

He had no sooner spoken than there was a loud CRACK! followed by a sharp cry from the builder. One of the floorboards had given way under his weight and his foot had gone straight through. The very next moment, Blister let out a startled yell as he stared towards the wall directly in front of him. As if in slow motion, the great wooden bookcase tumbled forward, falling . . . falling . . . falling!

On the other side of the gap, the Professor, his nephew and the builder's son leapt backwards as the bookcase crashed down and another cloud of swirling, choking dust gushed through the hole in the wall and filled the room.

Did You Know?

🦉 Englishman Howard Carter discovered the tomb of Tutankhamun, the Boy King of Egypt, on 4th November 1922.

🦉 Howard Carter was working for Lord Carnarvon, who was very rich and the owner of a valuable collection of Egyptian treasures.

🦉 Tutankhamun was only 9 years old when he became Pharaoh. He died at the age of 18, most probably from an infection following a broken leg, although it has been suggested that he may have been murdered by his jealous Uncle Ay, who then became Pharaoh.

🦉 It was reported that there was a warning engraved on the outside of Tutankhamun's tomb. It read:
'Death Shall Come on Swift Wings to Him Who Disturbs the Peace of the King.'

🐺 Rumours grew that the tomb was cursed and sensational headlines appeared in many of the newspapers at the time.

🐺 A few months after the tomb was opened, Lord Carnarvon was taken ill and rushed to a hospital in Cairo. He never recovered and many people said that his death was due to *the curse of the pharaoh's tomb.*

🐺 It is reported that at the exact time Lord Carnarvon died, all the lights went out in Cairo due to a power cut. Back home in England, Lord Carnarvon's favourite dog let out a terrible howl and dropped dead.

Chapter 2
The Wooden Chest

Blister the builder groaned in pain as three curious faces stared at him through the gap in the bedroom wall. He was lying flat on his back with the heavy wooden bookcase on top of him. He looked like a star fish. Two feet stuck out from the sides of the bookcase and his arms were stretched out behind him.

'Are you all right, Dad?' asked Alfie, sounding concerned. He was still clutching his bag of crisps.

'Well, of course I'm not all right!' grunted Blister, through gritted teeth. 'Will somebody get this great thing off me! I can't breathe properly!'

'After you,' said Alfie, standing aside for Nigel.

'No, you go first,' replied Nigel. 'After all, he's your father.'

'For goodness sake!' groaned Blister, his eyes bulging in disbelief. 'Get me out of here!'

The Professor took charge. Wiping the dust from his glasses, he squeezed through the gap and stepped into the secret room.

'It's incredible,' he said, glancing around the small dark room. 'It's been here all these years and no one knew it even existed!'

'But why would Howard Carter build a secret room in his house?' asked Nigel, joining his uncle. 'I don't understand?'

'Neither do I at the moment,' agreed Professor Nutter. 'That's a mystery we'll have to solve.'

'Excuse me . . . ' interrupted a feeble voice from the floor. 'Haven't you forgotten something? I'm still here, you know!'

'Oh, sorry!' said the Professor, staring down at the builder. Blister was breathing heavily and his face was as red as a beetroot. 'We'll have this bookcase off you in no time at all. Come on, Nigel.'

It was as the Professor bent down to lift the bookcase that he saw the box. There it was - a small, dark, wooden chest covered in dust, pushed into a gap near the bottom of the wall, so that it looked like any other brick.

'I don't believe it!' said the Professor, edging forward. His voice trembled with excitement. 'Look what I've found, Nigel! This room is beginning to give up its secrets!'

The Professor reached forward with both hands. Slowly, carefully, he withdrew the dusty chest from its hiding place and held it out in front of him, his eyes wide in anticipation.

'What is it?' hissed Alfie, peering through the gap in the wall.

'It looks like a pirate's treasure chest,' explained Nigel, 'only it's really small.'

'Now I know how Howard Carter felt when he discovered the treasures of Tutankhamun's tomb,' sighed the Professor. 'Who knows what we'll find inside the chest.'

'Will someone pl-eeease get me out of here!' sobbed the distraught builder. 'I don't think I've got long to live!'

△ ▽ △

Back in the bedroom, Professor Nutter placed the precious wooden chest on a small bedside table and stared at it in wonder. It did indeed look like a miniature treasure chest, dark wood with metal braids around the outside and a small metal clasp fastening the lid. He leaned forward and blew the dust from the chest and touched it ever so gently with his fingertips.

Meanwhile, Blister the builder was recovering on the Professor's bed. He was breathing more easily and his face had taken on a more normal colour.

'A fat lot of good you were!' grumbled

Blister, pointing an accusing finger at Alfie.
'I didn't see you rush to help when your poor
father was lying injured. What have you got
to say for yourself?'

'Would you like a crisp?' replied Alfie,
sheepishly, holding out the half empty
packet. 'They're salt 'n vinegar; my
favourite.'

'Are you going to open the box, Uncle?' asked Nigel. 'You can't keep us waiting much longer.'

'Yes, I'm going to open the box,' confirmed the Professor, nodding his head. 'I'm definitely going to open the box!'

Did You Know?

- When Howard Carter broke through into Tutankhamun's tomb, Lord Carnarvon asked him: 'Can you see anything?' Howard Carter paused and then replied: 'Yes, wonderful things!' The tomb was about to give up its secrets. There was, indeed, a treasure trove of untold riches.

- Although Tutankhamun's tomb was smaller than many of the other pharaoh's tombs, it was filled with around 3,500 individual items. There were paintings, statues, pieces of jewellery, chairs, caskets and a golden throne.

- Inside the burial chamber, Howard Carter discovered three golden coffins nested within each other. Inside the final coffin was the mummy of the Boy King Tutankhamun.

✸ A beautiful death mask was found inside the coffin containing the mummy of Tutankhamun. The mask, made in the image of the Boy King, is made of solid gold and inlaid with precious gems.

✸ By 1929, eleven people connected with the discovery of Tutankhamun's tomb had died. However, Howard Carter did not seem to be affected by the so called curse; he lived to the age of sixty-six and he died naturally.

Chapter 3
A Message from the Grave

Professor Nutter flicked open the
metal clasp and carefully raised the dark,
wooden lid. He peered into the box and his
eyes widened as his mouth fell slowly open.

'Well, w-w-what is it?' stuttered Nigel.
'Is it a huge diamond or a golden ring? Are
we going to be rich for the rest of our
lives?'

'Not exactly,' replied the Professor, slowly shaking his head, 'but it's very, very interesting.'

He reached into the box and withdrew a faded, folded envelope. The once white envelope had browned with age and it looked worn around the edges.

'It's an envelope,' said Alfie, helpfully. 'Even I can see it's an envelope.'

The Professor opened the flap and pulled out a piece of paper that had also been carefully folded into half and then folded once again. He unfolded it and then peered at it with interest.

'Hmmm . . . ' he said, rubbing his chin. 'Somebody has left a message and drawn part of a map. It's a bit faded but it's clearly a map.'

'What does the message say?' asked Nigel, his voice barely a whisper.

Alfie had stopped eating his crisps and was staring open mouthed at the Professor. Blister the builder had pulled himself up into a sitting position.

'It appears to be some sort of riddle,' said the Professor, studying the wrinkled sheet of paper. In fact, there are two riddles. The first one says:

Should you discover the secret room,
Beware the curse of the pharaoh's tomb!
For precious idols and golden rings
Lie buried deep in The Valley of the Kings!'

'The curse of the pharaoh's tomb!' repeated Nigel, taking a gulp. 'I don't like the sound of that!'

Professor Nutter glanced up, his eyes glinting with excitement.

'It's a message, Nigel! Don't you see - Howard Carter has left us a message from the grave! Look, he's left his initials at the bottom of the page!'

The Professor held up the map and jabbed his finger towards the bottom left hand corner. Sure enough, the initials H.C. were there for all to see.

'Where's The Valley of the Kings?' asked Nigel, innocently. 'Is it in Wales?'

'No, you bonehead! The Valley of the Kings is in Egypt!' snapped the Professor. 'It's where all of the pharaoh's were buried. Howard Carter is telling us that there is still an undiscovered tomb full of precious idols and golden rings. It's here, Nigel, marked on the map! The second riddle tells us exactly where to find the entrance! This could make us rich beyond belief and famous forever!'

"But what about the curse of the pharaoh's tomb?' repeated Nigel. 'That could make me scared stiff and dead forever!'

'Nonsense!' hissed the Professor. 'There is no such thing as a curse! These things are said to frighten people away. I don't know how anyone could be taken in by such rubbish!'

'Did you say rich beyond belief?' asked Blister the builder. He no longer looked injured in any way. He was licking his lips with greed.

'That's right,' confirmed Professor Nutter. He decided not to read out the second riddle. That would remain his secret for a little while longer. 'But you must not say a word to anyone! If you can keep our little secret I will make sure you get a nice little reward! You'll be able to buy as many packets of crisps as you want, Alfie! In fact, you'll be able to buy a whole crisp factory!'

'I'd like that!' said Alfie, nodding his head and licking his lips at the thought.

'Come on, Nigel,' said the Professor, picking up the chest and heading for the bedroom door. 'There's no time to waste. We've got plans to make.'

'Plans to make?' repeated Nigel, looking blank. 'What sort of plans, Uncle?'

'Well, isn't it obvious, you foolish boy? We're going to Egypt!' The Professor was trembling with excitement. 'This is the chance of a lifetime, Nigel! We're going to The Valley of the Kings to find the pharaoh's tomb and we're going to return with riches beyond belief!'

Did You Know

* **Warning:** *Do not read this section if you are about to eat your dinner!*

✠ Embalming was a way of preserving a body after death. The Ancient Egyptians embalmed the bodies of their pharaohs because they believed they needed their earthly bodies to take with them to the afterlife.

✠ A body ready for embalming would be taken to a place known as *'The Beautiful House'*, which would be near a temple. The body would be laid out and the vital organs removed. Firstly, a hooked instrument would be pushed up the nose and the brain would be pulled out. The internal organs would then be removed but the heart was replaced inside the body, along with spices and linen soaked in sweet smelling oils.

✢ The body was wrapped in hundreds of metres of linen. Good luck charms were placed in with the linen. Finally, the linen would be sealed with resin, a death mask was put over the face and the mummy was placed in its coffin.

✢ The organs removed from the dead pharaoh's body were placed in sealed containers called canopic jars. These canopic jars were placed inside the tomb along with the coffin.

✢ The pharaohs' tombs contained everything they would need for their journey to the afterlife. There was food and drink and games were even left inside the tombs. Mummified cats have been found so that the pharaoh's could take their favourite pets with them!

Chapter 4
Into Egypt

It was hot. It was very hot. In fact, it was boiling hot! Professor Nutter and his nephew Nigel had arrived in Egypt. It was exactly three months since their fantastic discovery of the old, wooden box containing the map. Planning the expedition had been quite easy but actually finding the pharaoh's tomb could prove to be much more difficult, even with Howard Carter's map and notes.

The two of them were sitting at a small glass table in the hotel lobby sipping ice cold drinks. The Professor's briefcase containing the precious map was at his feet.

'I've found someone we can trust,' said Professor Nutter, keeping his voice low so that no one would overhear them. 'I've set up a meeting. He should be here any minute.'

The Professor had no sooner spoken than a tall, well built man wearing traditional Egyptian dress, complete with head scarf, walked across the lobby and stood before them.

He reached out a hand and with a broad grin, which revealed a golden tooth, he said: 'Professor Nutter? I am so pleased to meet you!'

'Ah, come and join us, Farouk,' said the Professor, shaking his hand vigorously, 'and let me introduce you to my nephew, Nigel.'

Nigel smiled politely and took another gulp of his drink. He was fascinated by the man's golden tooth.

'I understand you would like a guide?' said Farouk, sitting down opposite the Professor. 'I'm told you are interested in the tombs in The Valley of the Kings?'

'One tomb in particular,' said the Professor, 'but before we go any further, I must swear you to secrecy. You must not breathe a word of anything you hear today. Do you understand?'

'You have my word,' replied Farouk, placing a hand on his heart – but Nigel thought he noticed a glint of deceit in the man's eye.

'Very well,' continued the Professor, and he lifted his briefcase onto the small drinks table and clicked open the lock.

Professor Nutter withdrew the faded map and spread it out on the table. Farouk leaned even closer.

'This map,' began the Professor, 'was drawn by the great explorer Howard Carter. It shows the tomb of the Pharaoh Tutakhahorn. He lies buried in The Valley of the Kings, his tomb undisturbed for thousands of years and, with your help, Farouk, I am going to uncover the tomb! I'll be as famous as Howard Carter! I can see the headlines now:

NUTTER ENTERS PHARAOH'S TOMB!

What do you say to that, my man! What do you say?'

Farouk's eyes widened in horror, his face turned deathly pale, his breath came in gasps and a damp sweat broke out on his forehead. He rose to his feet and shook his head. He opened his mouth but no words came out.

Eventually, his voice trembling with fear, he gasped in a hoarse whisper: 'We cannot enter the burial chamber of Tutakhahorn! It is protected by the curse of the pharaoh's tomb! Everyone knows the chamber is cursed! I will never go near it!'

'But you could be rich for the rest of your life,' urged the Professor. He jabbed a finger towards the map. 'Look, the riddle speaks of untold riches!'

'Perhaps I'll reconsider,' said Farouk, sitting back down, quickly. 'Let me see the map.'

The Egyptian studied the faded map, turning it this way and that way. He grunted a few times, rubbed his chin and tapped his gold tooth. Eventually, he glanced up and gave a greedy grin.

'I will do it!' he announced. 'I will *lead* you to the lost tomb of Tutakhahorn – but I will not enter the burial chamber; you do that alone. Agreed?'

'Agreed!' said the Professor, and the two men shook hands as Nigel drained his drink and gulped at the thought of the curse of the pharaoh's tomb.

Did You Know

◈ If you look at a map you will see that Egypt is in the very north of Africa. The Ancient Egyptians were originally hunters who settled along the banks of the River Nile and learned how to grow crops.

◈ At first, there were two separate parts to Egypt – Upper and Lower Egypt. Around 3,100 years BC the two parts became a single country ruled by a king known as a pharaoh.

◈ Without the River Nile, the civilization of Ancient Egypt would not have existed. Egypt is a hot, dry country with virtually no rain. Every year in mid-July, the River Nile flooded, leaving behind a rich layer of black mud, which was ideal for growing crops.

꩜ The most important crops grown were wheat and barley. Seeds were planted in October and harvested in March or April. Vegetables were also grown – especially onions, which were very important to the Egyptians. A pharaoh was often buried holding an onion in his hand! Grapes were grown and made into wine.

꩜ Farmers also kept animals, such as sheep, cattle, goats and pigs. The animals would be brought down to the fields after the harvest so that they could graze on the stubble.

Chapter Five
The Ship of the Desert

The following morning, Nigel and the
Professor met Farouk at the entrance to the
hotel. The guide stared at the two English
tourists and shook his head in dismay. They
were both dressed in Khaki shorts and
matching short sleeved shirts. Nigel was
wearing a baseball cap that seemed a size
too large and he carried a backpack that
contained two bottles of water, a packet of
biscuits and a small torch.

The Professor had chosen a floppy hat with a wide brim. He looked as if he was going to watch a cricket match.

'Dear, dear, dear,' said Farouk, with a sly smile on his face, 'that is not the best way to dress for a ride into the desert!'

'Why not?' asked Nigel innocently. 'We've put some sun cream on as well, you know.'

'Those shorts,' said Farouk, still shaking his head. 'It will be too easy for the flies and the mosquitoes. I fear they will have a feast!'

Nigel gulped and his eyes widened. He looked down at his knobbly knees but it was too late. There was nothing he could do about it.

'Let's just get on with it, shall we?' said the Professor. 'It's going to be a long and exciting day.'

'Follow me to our transport,' said Farouk. 'Be sure to keep close; the streets are very crowded even at this time of the morning.'

They set off at a brisk pace, away from the cool shade of the hotel and into the noisy, busy streets. They passed through a bazaar, colourful and crowded. There were all sorts of stalls selling delicious hot food, dried fruits and spices, pots and pans, carpets and rugs.

Professor Nutter and Nigel were struggling to keep up with Farouk as he darted in between the stalls, shouting a greeting and waving at people he knew.

Leaving the bazaar, Farouk suddenly turned into a narrow alley, which had high walls and a strange smell, like a pile of used socks waiting to be washed.

'Nearly there,' he said, glancing back to make sure that Nigel and the Professor were still with him. 'Our transport should be ready and waiting for us at the other end of the alley.'

Sure enough, the alley opened up into a large dusty square. Farouk stopped suddenly and Nigel and the Professor walked into the back of him.

'That is my jeep across the road,' announced Farouk, pointing proudly towards a rather old and battered grey vehicle.

'Excellent!' said Nigel, taking a step forward. 'Can I sit in the front? I don't travel very well.'

'And over there are my brother's camels,' said Farouk, grabbing hold of Nigel's arm. 'Our transport into the desert!'

Nigel froze like a statue and stared across the road and beyond the jeep. Sure enough, four huge camels were standing there tethered together, with their owner waving wildly to attract attention.

The Professor couldn't speak. He just stood there with his mouth wide open.

'I – I'm sorry . . . ' stuttered Nigel. 'You can't be serious? Surely you're not expecting me to climb onto one of those creatures?'

'But of course,' said Farouk, sounding surprised. 'I thought you'd be pleased. It is much better to travel by camel. The camel is the ship of the desert!'

'The ship of the desert . . . ' repeated Nigel, as they walked across the square towards the waiting beasts. He was sure one of them was staring straight at him. 'In that case I feel sea sick! I don't get on very well with animals. I'm even allergic to cats!'

'This is my brother Asim,' said Farouk, ignoring Nigel's whining. 'He knows the desert like the back of his hand. He will lead us straight to the area of the lost tomb.'

Asim gave a low bow and then shook the Professor's hand.

'Very pleased to meet you,' he said. 'I have heard all about your fantastic discovery. Riches beyond belief!'

'Yes, well let's hope so,' said the Professor, keeping one eye on the nearest camel, which seemed very bad tempered. 'Let's take a look at the map, should we – and then we can get started.'

△ ▽ △

Five minutes later, it was time to mount the camels. Nigel was beginning to feel ill. His face had turned green and sweat was pouring from his brow.

'There's nothing to worry about,' said Farouk, reassuringly. 'I'll get the camel to kneel down and you can just climb into the saddle. You'll be fine as long as you hold on tight.'

Sure enough, the camel knelt down and Nigel took a step forward. The beast turned

its head and stared at him, as if daring the
boy to climb on board.

The camel's breath smelled like a swamp.

'Ughh!' gasped Nigel, holding his nose.
'That animal seriously needs a dentist!'

Eventually, after several minutes of
fuss, Nigel managed to scramble into the
saddle, where he held on for dear life. The
Professor coped surprisingly well. He looked

quite confident and he seemed to be enjoying himself.

'Off we go, then!' announced Asim.

The four camels rose from their knees to their feet. Nigel was terrified. His animal took two steps forward, Nigel let out a yell, wobbled violently and then fell off immediately!

Did You Know?

- There are two different types of camels. The *dromedary* has just one hump while the *bactrian* has two humps. It is the dromedary camel that is common to Egypt.

- The dromedary camel is known as *'the ship of the desert'*. It is perfectly adapted to cope with the harsh desert environment. In the past, it was used to carry people and heavy loads across the hot, dry desert.

- Camels are very well designed to live and travel in the desert. They have long, thick eyelashes that protect them from the stinging, wind-blown sand; their nostrils can be partly closed and they have padded feet which stops them from sinking into the soft sand. They also have a pale yellow coat that blends in with the desert sand.

🐪 A camel can survive for up to two weeks without food or water. It can lose water from its body equal to a quarter of its total weight! To make up for this, a camel can drink a huge amount of water – up to 20 gallons in one go!

🐪 Camels have a reputation for being stubborn and bad-tempered. They do, indeed, spit and make strange grunting noises as if they are always complaining but they are generally good tempered animals.

Chapter Six
The Valley of the Kings

The camel ride into The Valley of the Kings took about an hour and Nigel moaned and groaned for most of the journey.

They travelled at a steady pace, Farouk and Asim leading the way into the dry desert valley.

On and on they went, past previously discovered tombs towards the most famous site of all – the tomb of Tutankhamun, the Boy King of Egypt. That was the area in which Howard Carter had been working; that was the area in which the new, hidden tomb was marked on the map, the entrance through the rock covered by a workman's hut.

Would it still be there?

Perhaps the hut had been removed years ago, after Howard Carter had drawn the map, and the tomb would never be found.

The Professor's heart began to beat faster and faster as they approached the entrance to Tutankhamun's tomb. A crowd of people waited in line to view the famous site. And then the Professor's heart surged and raced as, a couple of hundred metres beyond the tomb, he spotted an old, ruined workman's hut.

The roof had collapsed and one of the sides had fallen in but it was there! The hut was still there!

Asim guided the camels towards the hut and dismounted.

'Get me down!' wailed Nigel. 'I've never felt so ill in all my life! I think I'm going to die!'

Once Nigel had stopped being sick, he cheered up no end.

'Nothing to it!' he said, taking a deep breath. 'Wait until I tell them back home that I've ridden a camel!'

'Very good,' sighed the Professor in frustration. 'Now, can we get on with things, please?'

The Professor withdrew the map from his pocket and unfolded it carefully. Farouk and Asim leaned over his shoulder and stared at the faded sheet of paper.

'Yes, this is definitely the spot,' confirmed the Professor, his voice trembling with excitement, and he read out loud the second riddle, the one he had been keeping secret until this very moment:

Past the entrance to the tomb of Tut,
Through the door of the workman's hut.
Beneath the window can be found,
Sixteen steps leading underground.'

Farouk and Asim glanced at each other, nervously.

'Come on, then,' said the Professor, 'let's go and take a look inside the hut.'

It was Farouk's turn to go green. His hands began to shake and his bottom lip quivered.

'We go no further,' he said, his voice no more than a hoarse whisper. 'We will not risk the pharaoh's curse!'

'Pharaoh's curse!' mocked Nigel. He was feeling much bolder now that he was off the camel. 'My uncle says there is no such thing as a pharaoh's curse!'

'We go no further,' repeated Farouk. 'We will leave the shovels and return for you in exactly four hours.'

And with that, Asim untied the shovels from the back of his camel's saddle and handed them over to the Professor.

'Four hours,' repeated Professor Nutter. 'Four hours that could make history!'

The brothers turned and led the camels away, leaving Nigel and the Professor standing alone outside the ruined hut, sweltering in the morning sun.

'There's no time to lose,' said the Professor, passing a shovel to Nigel. 'We have work to do!'

Professor Nutter led the way into the hut. For some reason, even though one of the walls had fallen in, he entered through the door, pushing it open and stepping inside.

It was bone dry and dusty. There was a pile of splintered timber on the floor in the middle of the hut, fallen from the collapsed roof. Apart from that, the hut was completely empty. The professor glanced around quickly and then pointed in excitement.

'Look over there, Nigel! That must be the window that's mentioned in the riddle!'

'Ooh, yes,' said Nigel, nodding his head. 'Shall we have a look out of it?'

'Of course not, you bonehead!' snapped the Professor. 'We need to search for the entrance to the tomb beneath the window.'

They moved across the hut towards the window, stepping over the piles of dry timber. The Professor checked the map once more and then stamped on the ground.

'It feels absolutely solid,' he said, in disappointment. 'Let's get to work with the shovels.'

Outside the hut, no more than a few hundred metres back, two suspicious figures watched and waited in interest.

The Professor plunged his shovel into the floor and the blade sank into a layer of soft sand.

'Come on,' he urged his nephew, 'put some effort into it, Nigel.'

Nigel removed his backpack and got to work. The two of them delved into the ground, shovelling the sand to one side and then delving again. Deeper and deeper they went until they were standing in a hole wide enough to move around in. They were drenched in sweat and completely exhausted.

'It's no good!' gasped Nigel. He was so red he looked as if he was about to burst. 'There's nothing here, Uncle! Nothing but more sand!'

In sheer frustration, Nigel thrust his shovel into the ground one final time – and jumped back in surprise as it cracked against something solid.

'Did you hear that?' asked the Professor. 'That wasn't sand, it was rock or stone or . . . something!'

They scraped at the ground with their shovels, working quicker than ever, pushing aside the fine, red sand to reveal a solid stone slab set firmly into a bed of rock.

The Professor was almost beside himself.

'We've found the entrance!' he screeched. 'We've found the entrance to the pharaoh's tomb!'

'Yes, we've found the entrance! We've found the entrance!' yelled Nigel, just as excited.

They didn't notice that the moment they uncovered the entrance to the tomb the blistering, still day seemed suddenly to change. They didn't notice that a hot, dry wind was blowing, or that the sky was turning darker and darker by the second . . .

Did You Know?

๑ The Ancient Egyptians firstly built pyramids as final resting places for their pharaohs. Pyramids were designed to protect the pharaohs' bodies forever as their spirits journeyed to the afterlife.

๑ The most famous pyramids are the three Great Pyramids at Giza, near Cairo. However, more than eighty pyramids were built in total.

๑ All of the pyramids were built on the west bank of the River Nile – the side on which the sun sets. The four walls of a pyramid had to face exactly north, south, east and west. The pyramids were built by craftsmen together with thousands of slaves.

෨ Inside the pyramid, the pharaoh's body was laid to rest in a central burial chamber. The burial chamber was always exactly beneath the point of the pyramid.

෨ The huge pyramids meant that everyone knew where the pharaohs were buried. It was too easy for robbers to break into the pyramids and steal the treasures. Eventually, the Ancient Egyptians stopped building pyramids and buried their pharaohs in tombs cut into the rock in secret places in The Valley of the Kings.

Chapter Seven
The Pharaoh's Tomb

It took them another half hour to release the stone slab. Using their shovels as levers, they pushed and they strained and they twisted until the huge slab gave way and they were able to force it to one side, just enough to reveal the entrance to the dark tomb.

'That will do nicely,' panted the Professor. 'We can squeeze through the gap.

Get your torch, Nigel.'

Nigel climbed out of the hole they had dug in the floor of the hut, ready to fetch the torch he had brought in his backpack. It was then that he felt the blast from the hot desert wind and, looking around in panic, he saw the dark, angry sky.

'W - what's happened?' he stammered. 'W - where's the sun gone?'

The Professor peered out from the deep hole to see Nigel clutching his backpack and shaking like a leaf.

'The sky has turned black,' continued Nigel, 'just as we've opened the pharaoh's tomb! You don't think it's . . . the curse, do you?'

'Of course it's not the curse, you stupid boy!' snapped the Professor. 'It's a sandstorm! You often get sandstorms in the desert, although I do admit there's usually more warning. Fetch the torch, Nigel. We can take shelter down in the tomb.'

Nigel gulped and took a deep breath. He wasn't convinced.

Professor Nutter shone the torch deep into the entrance of the tomb. There were steps, steep stone steps leading downwards.

'Come along, Nigel,' said the excited Professor. 'This is going to be the discovery of our lives!'

The Professor led the way, squeezing through the small gap left by the stone slab. He moved slowly, counting the steps down, fourteen, fifteen, sixteen – and then they were in a narrow passage with a low roof.

'I don't like it,' whined Nigel. 'I've got a phobia about enclosed spaces!'

'Don't be so soft!' snapped the Professor. 'This should lead us to the burial chamber.'

The passage twisted and turned and then suddenly came to an end. Carved into the rock in front of them was the entrance to the burial chamber. It had been sealed with plaster but had crumbled with age, so that there was a gap in the bottom left hand corner wide enough to crawl through.

'Just look at that!' exclaimed the Professor, moving his torch up and down. 'It's wonderful, Nigel!'

Painted onto the sealed entrance was a faded picture of a pharaoh sitting on a golden throne. There were some strange signs beneath the picture, which the Professor recognised immediately.

'The picture is obviously the pharaoh, Tutakhahorn,' explained the Professor, 'and the signs beneath are hieroglyphics, Ancient

Egyptian writing. I should be able to tell you
what it says.'

The Professor studied the signs closely
and then suddenly took a step back. His
hand started to shake and he almost
dropped the torch.

'What's the matter?' asked Nigel. 'What does it say?'

The Professor's bottom lip quivered.

'I've seen it before,' he said. 'The same message was found in Tutankhamun's tomb. It says: *Death Shall Come on Swift Wings to he who Disturbs the Peace of the King.*'

'Let's go!' said Nigel, turning and making his way back along the passage.

'No, wait!' urged the Professor. 'We've come this far, we must enter the burial chamber!'

And with that, the Professor got down on all fours and crawled through the gap. Nigel followed, not wanting to be left alone.

As they stood up, the two visitors in the pharaoh's tomb gasped in amazement.

The Professor let the torch beam explore the walls, which were covered from top to bottom with detailed drawings. There were pictures of Egyptian gods, hunting scenes and great feasts.

The beam of light moved down to the floor and the Professor gasped again. There were broken pots and plates scattered everywhere. There were two ancient wooden wheels and several smashed stone statues – but there was no sign anywhere of any gold or jewels or untold riches.

'It's been robbed,' muttered the Professor. 'We're not the first ones to enter the tomb, Nigel – it has already been robbed of its riches.'

The Professor was so shocked he couldn't speak for a moment. And then he

noticed it. Propped up against the back wall
of the burial chamber was a heavy, wooden
coffin. The lid had been removed and the
coffin was empty. The mummy was missing.

To the right of the coffin was a small,
wooden table and on top of the table was a

single dagger with a golden handle. At least that could be worth something.

'I don't understand,' said the Professor, scratching his head. 'Why would tomb robbers steal the pharaoh's body?'

But Nigel was not paying attention. He had heard something else; a grating, scraping sound, followed by heavy footsteps. Slowly and fearfully, he turned and pointed towards the entrance of the tomb.

'It's – it's in the passageway!' he stammered. 'It's coming towards us! It must be the mummy seeking revenge! It's the curse of the pharaoh's tomb!'

Did You Know?

ㄱ We have learned a lot about the Ancient Egyptians from the paintings decorating the walls of the pharaohs' tombs and from the items discovered inside the tombs.

ㄱ Tomb paintings often show scenes of hunting, which was very popular with rich Egyptians. Other pictures show gods, such as *Re* (or *Ra*), the sun god or *Osiris*, the ruler of the dead. Scenes of feasts and banquets with dancers, acrobats and musicians show how rich Egyptians were entertained.

ㄱ There were always pictures or engravings of the pharaohs inside their tombs. These show us how the pharaohs dressed. An engraving found inside Tutankhamun's tomb shows the young king sitting on a throne with his wife at his side. The queen is wearing a head-dress decorated with tall ostrich feathers.

The Ancient Egyptians liked to wear jewellery, especially rings, necklaces and earrings. Jewellery belonging to the pharaohs would be buried along with them for their journey to the afterlife, often wrapped in amongst the linen wound around the body.

Chapter Eight
The Golden Dagger

Professor Nutter and Nigel stared towards the sealed entrance of the tomb. Sure enough, the beam from the Professor's torch picked out shadows in the passage beyond the gap. As they watched, their pulses racing, their hearts pounding, a pair of hands appeared in the gap and the strangest of figures crawled through into the burial chamber. Both the Professor and Nigel took a step back as the figure stood up and faced them. It was not what they expected. The figure was dressed in long, flowing Egyptian robes and a dark hood covered its head so that its face could not be seen.

'Who are you? What do you want?' The Professor's voice was trembling with fear.

The hooded figure did not reply. Ever so slowly, it raised an arm and pointed.

'It wants us to move out of the way,' whimpered Nigel. 'Let's do what it says!'

The Professor and Nigel stood to one side as the figure advanced towards the pharaoh's coffin. And then the Professor remembered the dagger. He edged slowly towards the small wooden table as the mysterious figure, now with its back to them, stood before the empty coffin.

And then, suddenly, there was a sneeze, followed by a second sneeze and then a third. It was so strange. The Professor had not sneezed, Nigel had not sneezed and the hooded figure certainly had not sneezed – and yet someone had sneezed. Nigel nudged the Professor and pointed to the gap and to their amazement, a second figure crawled through. It looked exactly the same as the first one, only smaller.

The hooded figure spun round as the Professor grabbed the golden dagger and hid it behind his back.

'You fool!' hissed the figure, as the newcomer stood in the shadows. 'I told you to wait in the passage!'

Nigel thought he recognised the voice but he wasn't sure.

'I'm sorry, Dad,' said the newcomer, trying to stifle another sneeze, 'I was frightened. I wanted to see what was going on.'

The newcomer stepped forward and, as he did so, something fell from his robes and floated to the floor. Instinctively, the Professor moved his torch and the beam settled on . . . an  empty crisp packet . . . salt 'n vinegar flavour.

'It's you!' gasped Nigel. 'It's you and your father!'

Blister the builder instantly pulled the hood back from his head and snarled at Nigel and the Professor.

'Did you really think we were going to sit back and let you take all the riches from the pharaoh's tomb? Did you really think we were so stupid?'

Nigel did not answer. He was still staring at Alfie, who had also removed his hood.

'We followed you to Egypt,' continued Blister, his greedy eyes glinting red in the dark tomb. 'We even booked in to the same hotel, disguised, of course – and we watched from a distance as you entered the workman's hut and uncovered the entrance to the tomb.'

'But you've wasted your time,' said Professor Nutter. He was still clutching the golden dagger behind his back. 'There are no untold riches. The tomb has already been robbed!'

'That's all the worse for you!' stormed Blister, raising his hands in anger. 'We can't let you out of here alive!'

'Oh, I think you can,' said the Professor, calmly. He withdrew the golden dagger from behind his back and gripped it firmly in his hand.

Shocked and surprised, Blister took a step back and his foot caught the bottom edge of the empty coffin. The pharaoh's coffin seemed to move away from the wall and lurch forward. Alfie gave a warning yell but it was too late. The heavy coffin crashed down on top of the startled builder, sending him tumbling to the floor and trapping him beneath.

Alfie rushed forward and fell to his knees in an effort to help.

'That's the second time he's been flattened,' said Nigel, thoughtfully. 'Perhaps there is such a thing as the pharaoh's curse.'

'Come on, Nigel,' said the Professor, 'let's get out of here.'

The two of them scrambled through the gap into the passageway, leaving Alfie struggling in the darkness to free his father.

Nigel and the Professor climbed the sixteen stone steps and squeezed through the narrow space to the side of the stone slab.

They were not sure how long they had been underground but the sandstorm had blown over. The burning sun was shining down once again from a clear, blue Egyptian sky and there, waiting for them outside the workman's hut, stood Farouk and Asim, together with four grumpy looking camels.

'Greetings!' said Farouk, and as he smiled, his golden tooth glinted in the bright sunlight. 'You found no Egyptian treasure, then?'

'Not exactly,' admitted the Professor, 'but I think you knew the tomb was empty, didn't you?'

'We came back to help you,' interrupted Asim. 'We saw those two strangers follow you into the tomb – but obviously you did not need our help!'

'No, I think we'll leave them down there to face the curse of the pharaoh's tomb,' said the Professor, 'for a little while, at least!'

They laughed. They laughed so loud that their laughter echoed deep down in the pharaoh's tomb and, as they walked away from the workman's hut, even the camels seemed to smile in satisfaction.

Also available in the Reluctant Reader Series from:

PUBLISHING

Sam's Spitfire Summer *(WW2 Adventure)*
Ian MacDonald   ISBN 978 1 905637 43 0

Alien Teeth   *(Humorous Science Fiction)*
Ian MacDonald   ISBN 978 1 905637 32 2

Eyeball Soup   *(Science Fiction)*
Ian MacDonald   ISBN 978 1 904904 59 5

Chip McGraw   *(Cowboy Mystery)*
Ian MacDonald   ISBN 978 1 905637 08 9

Close Call   *(Mystery - Interest age 12+)*
Sandra Glover   ISBN 978 1 905 637 07 2

Beastly Things in the Barn *(Humorous)*
Sandra Glover   ISBN 978 1 904904 96 0
www.sandraglover.co.uk

Cracking Up   *(Humorous)*
Sandra Glover   ISBN 978 1 904904 86 1

Deadline   *(Adventure)*
Sandra Glover   ISBN 978 1 904904 30 4

The Crash   *(Mystery)*
Sandra Glover   ISBN 978 1 905637 29 4

The Owlers   *(Adventure)*
Stephanie Baudet   ISBN 978 1 904904 87 8

The Curse of the Full Moon   *(Mystery)*
Stephanie Baudet   ISBN 978 1 904904 11 3

A Marrow Escape   *(Adventure)*
Stephanie Baudet   ISBN 1 900818 82 5

The One That Got Away   *(Humorous)*
Stephanie Baudet   ISBN 1 900818 87 6

The Haunted Windmill   *(Mystery)*
Margaret Nash   ISBN 978 1 904904 22 9

Trevor's Trousers   *(Humorous)*
David Webb   ISBN 978 1 904904 19

The Library Ghost   *(Mystery)*
David Webb   ISBN 978 1 904374 66

Dinosaur Day   *(Adventure)*
David Webb   ISBN 978 1 904374 67 1

Laura's Game   *(Football)*
David Webb   ISBN 1 900818 61 2

Grandma's Teeth   *(Humorous)*
David Webb   ISBN 978 1 905637 20 1

Friday the Thirteenth   *(Humorous)*
David Webb   ISBN 978 1 905637 37 9

The Bears Bite Back   *(Humorous)*
Derek Keilty   ISBN 978 1 905637 36 2

Order online @ **www.eprint.co.uk**